10 Steps to

Gardening
with
Nature

Using Sustainable Methods
to Replicate Mother Nature

by Carole Ann Rollins, PhD and Elaine Ingham, PhD

Published by:
Gardening With Nature　　Novato, California

10 Steps to Gardening With Nature
Using Sustainable Methods to Replicate Mother Nature
Authors: Carole Ann Rollins, PhD and Elaine Ingham, PhD

Copyright © 2011 by Carole Ann Rollins and Elaine Ingham

Book Design, Graphics, and Cover Art: Carole Ann Rollins, PhD

Distributed by:
Nature Technologies International LLC
14 Tilden Drive, Novato, CA 94947
Phone: 415-898-5895, Fax: 707-940-0444
www.nature-technologies.com, info@nature-technologies.com
and
Sustainable Studies Institute
635 SW Western Ave, Corvallis, OR 97333
Phone: 541-257-2614, Fax: 541-752-5142
www.sustainablestudies.org, info@sustainablestudies.org

Printed in the United States of America
First Printing June 2011
Paperback Edition: ISBN 0-9797561-4-6
Library of Congress Control Number: 2011925807

Contents

Preface

Overview Of Gardening With Nature

Acknowledgments

Thanking People For Their Contribution

Step One

Understanding What Gardening With Nature Means............................1

1-1. What is the basic underlying premise of Gardening With Nature? If I were to start Gardening With Nature, what would I be doing?.......3

1-2. What are the basic components of Gardening With Nature? Is there any one absolutely essential component that must be in place? 5

1-3. What do these beneficial organisms do? 5

1-4. How do these beneficial organisms contribute to Gardening With Nature? How do these organisms do their job? 6

1-5. How many of these beneficial organisms are necessary to carry out these jobs? 7

1-6. Do these organisms help my plant get the nutrients necessary for growth and health?..7

1-7. Do I need to feed any plants chemical fertilizers anymore?.................8
1-8. How is soil structure related to water and fertility? 8

Step Two

Assessing A Growing System **9**

2-1. Have I used pesticides, herbicides, or fungicides?. 10
2-2. Did those chemicals fix my problems? 10
2-3. Did any of the problems come back again?....................................11
2-4. How often do I apply chemicals to control problems 12
2-5. Did I use chemicals to combat weed problems?..............................12
2-6. Have I used chemical fertilizers? When was the last time?.................13
2-7. Do I know what chemical synthetic fertilizers are made from?...........13
2-8. Can I use chemical fertilizers when I Garden With Nature? 14
2-9. What will happen if I do use chemical fertilizers? 14

Step Three

**Using Environmentally Friendly
Gardening Products**.........................**15**

3-1. What gardening products will work best for Gardening
     With Nature?...16
3-2. What does *organic* mean? 16
3-3. What does an *organically-allowed* seal mean? 16
3-4. Are all organically-allowed products compatible with Gardening
     With Nature?...17
3-5. How can I test to see if the salt levels in a product are too high?.........17
3-6. What if the test shows that salt levels in a product are too high?.........17

Step Four

Determing A Plants' Health?..............19

4-1. What does a healthy plant look like? 20
4-2. What are the symptoms of unhealthy plants? 20
4-3. What if my plants' leaves are yellow and the plants are
     losing leaves?...21
4-4. Are there any tests for nutrient deficiency?...........................21
4-5. What is a disease-causing organism? What is a pest? 22
4-6. How do plants resist disease or pests?....................................22

Step Five

Preparing Soil 23

5-1. How do I prepare my soil for new plantings 24
5.2. How much organic matter should be in my soil.....................24
5-3. What kind of compost should I use? 26
5-4. What kind of plant-growing environment is necessary for
     healthy plants?...27
5-5. How do I start creating a Gardening With Nature
     environment in my yard? 28
5-6. Do I really have to add microbes? Can't I just use really good
     organic products?..28
5-7. How does nature achieve balance in the natural growing world?.........29
5-8. Will I ever have to rebalance my growing environment once it
     is established?..32

Step Six

Planting And Transplanting..............33

6-1. How do I plant new flowers, shrubs, and trees?....................33
6-2. How does mixing compost and soil help roots grow? 34
6-3. Should I feed my plants any food after transplanting? 35
6-4. How should I care for the soil after transplanting? 35
6-5. How should I prepare and plant seeds?....................36
6-6. How do I add beneficial organisms when planting gardens, crops, lawns, or pastures?....................36
6-7. What kind of balance of beneficial organisms do shrubs, perennial flowers, and herbs need? 36
6-8. What kind of balance of beneficial organisms do annual or biennial flowers need? 37
6-9. What do I use for a potting mix when planting annuals?....................38

Step Seven

Feeding Plants....................40

7-1. How often should I spray organic nutrients and microbes on plants? .39
7-2. How much organic nutrient should I give my trees?....................39
7-3. Will I be able to prevent and control diseases on my plants?....................40
7-4. If I have perfect growing conditions, what more do I need to do?....................41
7-5. If I do not have perfect growing conditions, what do I need to do?.....42
7-6. How much nutrient do I need to add if I am also using compost teas? 42
7-7. Do I need to add any inorganic synthetic chemicals? 43
7-8. How much compost or liquid compost should be used?....................43
7-9. Should I till the compost in?....................44
7-10. How can I use compost I made last year? 44
7-11. Can I add nutrients to my compost or mulch?....................44

7-12. Do I need to add inorganic synthetic chemical nutrients? 45
7-13. Do I need to send my growing medium to be tested for
     chemical analysis of N-P-K? 45
7-14. How many kinds of microorganisms do I need? 47

Step Eight

Fixing Problems 49

8-1. If I have poor soil, do these microbes help? 49
8-2. Does tilling my soil affect soil structure or the organisms? 50
8-3. What happens when my soil is compacted? 50
8-4. What happens when my plants can't get nutrients because
     my soil is compacted? 51
8-5. What if I see problems with my plants? 52
8-6. How can I fix nutrient deficiencies? 53
8-7. What should I do if the soil for my plants gets out of balance? 54
8-8. What should I do if the soil for my trees gets out of balance? 56
8-9. What should I do if toxic chemicals have been used and I have
     problems? 56
8-10. What happens to the toxic residuals from pesticides and
     inorganic fertilizers? 57
8-11. Can beneficial organisms help with degrading toxic residuals? 57
8-12. How many times do I need to apply beneficial organisms to
     eliminate the problems? 58
8-13. How fast will I see results after applying beneficial organisms? 59
8-14. What is the least expensive way to implement this recovery process? .60

Step Nine

Preparing For The Next Season 61

9-1. What should I do in the fall to prepare for winter? 62
9-2. What should I do in the spring to prepare for summer? 64

Step Ten

Checking The Quality Of Water 65

10-1. Does my water district use chlorine in my water?................................66
10-2. Is there a way I can test my water for chlorine myself?.......................66
10-3. What can I do if there is chlorine in my water?..................................67
10-4. Does my water district use chloramine in my water?..........................67
10-5. What can I do if there is chloramine in my water?.............................67
10-6. How much salt is in my water?..67

Notes

Explanations and Comments..............69

Index

Alphabethical Listing of Subjects 73

About the Authors

Biographical Information 79

Great things are done when men and mountains meet. ~ William Blake

Preface

Many people are demanding organic, based on political, nutritional, and environmental reasons. Implicit in the reason to return to natural production methods is the fact that beneficial organisms are killed by the use of toxic chemicals. This sets up toxic chemical users to need more and more and more toxic chemicals to maintain the system to the point that an addiction to those toxic chemicals is formed.

How do you "Just Say No" to that addiction? Switching from using synthetic chemical fertilizers and toxic pesticides to using organic products does not fix the problem caused by toxic chemicals. If we only use natural products that kill pests, weeds, or diseases, the problem has not been solved, and the "organic grower" will not be successful. "The switch" must involve a wholly new approach, which requires working with nature, instead of combatting and fighting nature.

In this book, we suggest that Gardening With Nature is preventative. We deal with the cause of diseases, pests, or poor fertility. The toxic chemical approach tries to suppress symptoms of the problem, instead of fixing the problem. By merely trying to suppress the symptoms, the problem typically gets worse and worse, which leads to more and more chemical use. This results in a loss of nutrients, as well as the toxic chemicals leaching from the soil and polluting our water systems. All this occurs because the beneficial soil life, which is normally present in healthy soil, is lost.

Chemical companies love people who mindlessly follow their instruction, never asking why growing food gets more and more expensive and involves ever greater amounts of ever more toxic chemicals. Since toxic chemicals do not deal with the problem, but rather with symptoms, we get drawn into a chemical downward spiral. If we try to stop toxic chemical use, our plants do not do well. Failure is often the result if we try to get off the downward spiral by simply shifting to using organic products.

In this book, we suggest that to win our freedom from toxic chemicals, we must start Gardening With Nature. The key to Gardening With Nature—to true organic gardening—is to recognize the power of beneficial microorganisms, elements little known or understood by the general public.

In wilderness I sense the miracle of life. ~ Charles A. Lindbergh

Organic growing is different from using chemicals for several important reasons. First, we need to have most of the nutrients present in the soil in non-leachable forms most of the time. We need to have the mechanisms in that soil to convert those not-available-to-plant nutrients into plant-available nutrients IN THE ROOT ZONE, for the most part, not away from the roots. The mechanisms to do this conversion process are beneficial microbes — bacteria, fungi, protozoa, nematodes, and microarthropods. The beneficial species, rather than the disease species, of these organisms are naturally found in healthy growing systems.

Simply putting down the highest quality, most expensive organic nutrients in your garden is not likely to result in great plant growth, unless the correct microbes are present. Beneficial bacteria and fungi are needed first to degrade any residual toxic chemicals in your growing environment. Then bacteria and fungi are needed to tie up nutrients so those nutrients are not leachable, and thus are not lost when water moves through the soil. Finally, bacteria and fungi need to be eaten by protozoa and nematodes to release tied-up nutrients in a plant-available form. If any of the species that do this processing in your soil are missing, then you need to get them back. If life is missing in your soil, you need to give Mother Nature a jump-start to help her reestablish the normal set of organisms, and thus, reestablish normal nutrient cycling.

Clearly this process involves more than simply laying down a set of mineral nutrients. We need to educate people to understand that plants can, indeed, take care of themselves without people getting in the way. There is no need to have complex feeding schedules and mind-boggling mathematical calculations on rates of adding nutrients or adjusting pH. In the Gardening With Nature approach, we provide nutrients and a diversity of microbes to transform those nutrients, and the plants do the rest. Microbes, then, hold on to nutrients and they no longer leach from the soil, so you can use far fewer nutrients. Microbes also restructure the soil by creating air passageways and cavities that enable water and air to be retained within the soil, so you use considerably less water. You save money, time, and energy, and the health of your plants improves. Plants contain more nutrients and have built up their immune systems to become resistant to problem pests and diseases, leading to higher yields and plants that grow bigger and faster.

Look deep into nature and then you will understand everything better.
~Albert Einstein

In this book, we also discuss some of the complications that can arise when Gardening With Nature. Most significantly, we describe the complications that arise because our gardens are not isolated. Though we have added microbes and organic nutrients, we still may have problems from environmental disturbances beyond our control—pesticide drift from a neighboring yard, acid rain, freezing weather, scorching heat, chlorine and chloramine in our watering systems, or too many salts. We must continue to tend our gardens and be watchful. We must continue to add microbes and nutrients. However, less maintenance will be required each year, as our soils increase in organic matter and microbe populations. Maintaining a healthy population of 70 percent of beneficial microbes in soils and on plant surfaces will nurture a protective type of environment that will thwart any disease-causing organisms that may come along, simply by outcompeting them for food and space.

It is our goal with this book to teach you how to truly Garden With Nature. In it, we offer practical guidelines for transitioning from chemical gardening to Gardening With Nature. It is hoped that the book will inspire you to reinvent your existing organic growing methods by using beneficial microorganisms to improve your plants' health.

Carole Ann Rollins, PhD, Novato, California
Elaine Ingham, PhD, Corvallis, Oregon

Those who dwell among the beauties and mysteries of the earth are never alone or weary of life. ~*Rachel Carson*

Earth and sky, woods and fields, lakes and rivers, the mountain and the sea, are excellent schoolmasters, and teach some of us more than we can ever learn from books. ~ John Lubbock

Acknowledgments

Finally, we wish to thank Ron Kaye, Connie Schmidt, and Holly Thesieres Monteith, MA, MAC, and ELS, for proofreading and editing and Mary Harper for indexing. Carole thanks James Eddington, Gladys Rollins, and Bernice Harray for all the unending and unwavering encouragement and support through the years.

In all things of nature there is something of the marvelous. ~ Aristotle

Understanding What Gardening with Nature Means

Understanding What Gardening With Nature Means: *Gardening With Nature means to garden in a way that is harmonious with nature.*

Gardening With Nature means to garden in a way that is harmonious with nature. The chemical approach to managing disease and pests is to try to prevent everything except the crop from existing in the system. Clearly that is impossible, and nature will fight back more and more every step of the way. Toxic chemicals have to get more and more toxic, until you end up getting rid of the people in the system. We aren't going to win this war against nature.

Instead, work with nature. Nature is easily moved in the direction she was already going. It can take nature a long time to develop the system that you want, but it is easy to help that natural progression. Once you have the system functioning with all the normal checks and balances, the system is sustainable.

That's what we will try to do in this publication.

Sustainable System: *Once you have the system functioning with all the normal checks and balances, the system is sustainable. We will provide practical advice on how to implement these principles in your own growing system.*

This book is in a question-and-answer format to help you look at your current gardening practices, understand the principles of Gardening With Nature, and explore different ways of implementing these principles. In this introductory chapter we will present the basic underlying theoretical principles of Gardening With Nature. In the remaining chapters, we provide practical advice on how to implement these principles in your own growing system.

QUESTION 1-1: *What is the basic underlying premise of Gardening With Nature? If I were to start Gardening With Nature, what would I be doing?*

ANSWER 1-1: First, understand the basics of the system you want to create. Work with Mother Nature to implement a natural biological system like those that have been performing successfully for eons. Return the beneficial life to your soil. Aerobic compost, made properly, can fix the needed balance in your soil.

Aerobic Compost: *Aerobic compost, made properly, can fix the needed balance in your soil. You can make compost at home or buy compost prepackaged or in bulk from your garden supply center.*

Once a balance is reached, the environment must be created and maintained so that the soil life can obtain all it needs to help rebuild soil structure and cycle nutrients. When that system is developed so that it maintains itself, the plants growing there will not be stressed: feng shui for the garden, if you will.

*Return
the
beneficial
life
to
your
soil.*

You will be re-creating a whole soil food web and ecosystem in your own backyard. You will be providing your plants with a way of growing that is compatible with nature. Gardening With Nature is about the soil you use, how you prepare the soil, what you add to the soil, and what you feed your plants. With the full diversity of life properly balanced, problems with diseases, weeds, and pests are eliminated.

Gardening With Nature is about the soil you use, how you prepare the soil, what you add to the soil, and what you feed your plants.

There will be pests that stray into healthy systems, but the cute little predators (good bugs) in the garden will deal with those pests long before they harm the plants. Gardening With Nature teaches you about growing environments and gardening practices for all types of plants, trees, grasses, shrubs, vines, flowers, and vegetables, whether in the ground, in containers, indoors, outdoors, or in greenhouses, rejuvenating, revitalizing, reestablishing, reintroducing, and replicating the ways of natural growing systems so that you can grow whatever kind of plant you desire by setting up the environment to let it flourish.

Gardening With Nature Is For All Types Of Plants: *Gardening With Nature teaches you about growing environments and gardening practices for all types of plants, trees, grasses, shrubs, vines, flowers, and vegetables—whether in the ground, in containers, indoors, outdoors, or in greenhouses.*

QUESTION 1-2: *What are the basic components of Gardening With Nature? Is there any one absolutely essential component that must be in place?*

ANSWER 1-2: Beneficial organisms are the basic components necessary to get this process rolling. There is a whole ecosystem of beneficial living organisms that are found naturally in your soil and on your plants that set the stage for certain plants, and not others, to grow. Manage the life in the soil, and the life will manage the growing system for the plant. Adhere to the principles of Gardening With Nature, and you will easily see the needed beneficial organisms in correct balances. Both bacteria and fungi are needed. In each group are "good guys" and "bad guys."

Beneficial
Bacteria And **Fungi**
The **"Good Guys"**

Non-Beneficial
Bacteria And **Fungi**
The **"Bad Guys"**

We will teach you how to prevent the "bad guys" from reaching such high numbers that they overwhelm and destroy your plants. If they do arrive, say, from your neighbor's yard, we will teach you how to deal with their arrival without using toxic chemicals. The "bad guys" will be dealt with by "miniature watchdogs" that are part of a properly functioning natural soil food web growing system.

QUESTION 1-3: *What do these beneficial organisms do?*

ANSWER 1-3: They perform many, many jobs that benefit productive growing systems. Beneficial organisms produce materials or create conditions that are beneficial for plant growth and health. These beneficial organisms help create strong and healthy plants that are naturally resistant to pests.

Beneficial organisms help create strong and healthy plants.

QUESTION 1-4: *How do these beneficial organisms contribute to Gardening With Nature? How do these organisms do their job?*

ANSWER 1-4: Certain species of bacteria and fungi, fed by the plant, form protective barriers around all plant surfaces. These protective barriers do not just consist of one set of species. Species vary with the area of the plant and even with the time of day. Root tips have one set of species functioning right now, but in an hour, a different set will dominate, and the same goes for root hairs, bark, or leaves. One thing that this complex set of bacteria and fungi does is to prevent disease and pest organisms from finding or reaching the plant. If "bad guys" can't find their host, they can't cause problems.

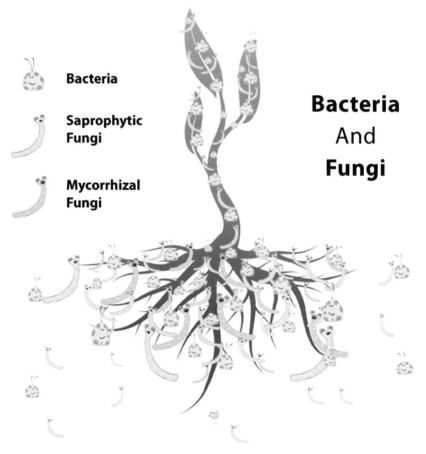

Bacteria

Saprophytic Fungi

Mycorrhizal Fungi

Bacteria And Fungi

Bacteria And Fungi Around Plant Surfaces: *Certain species of bacteria and fungi form protective barriers around all plant surfaces. One thing that this complex set of bacteria and fungi does is to prevent disease and pest organisms from finding or reaching the plant.*

QUESTION 1-5: *How many of these beneficial organisms are necessary to carry out these jobs?*

ANSWER 1-5: Diversity in and around all parts of the plant is required. Then, despite any changes in temperature, oxygen, calcium concentration, nitrogen concentration, water, and so on, there will always be a broad array of organisms protecting the plant surfaces, cycling nutrients, and building soil structure, under all types of environmental conditions.

QUESTION 1-6: *Do these organisms help my plant get the nutrients necessary for growth and health?*

ANSWER 1-6: These beneficial organisms do the nutrient cycling that produces the nutrients your plant needs, in the right kinds of forms, right there at the root or on the leaves, at the right times of year and in the right amounts. This is what nature set up and is the way natural ecosystems have been working for billions of years. Soil predators, like flagellates, amoebae, bacterial-feeding nematodes, fungal-feeding nematodes, earthworms, and microarthropods, consume bacteria and fungi and release the right forms of nutrients for your plants, that is, plant-available N, P, K, Ca, Na, B, Si, Co, Fe, and so on.

Soil Predators

Flagellates **Amoebae** **Bacterial-Feeding Nematodes**

Fungal-Feeding Nematodes **Earthworms** **Microarthropods**

Soil Predators: *Flagellates, amoebae, bacterial-feeding nematodes, fungal-feeding nematodes, earthworms, and microarthropods are soil predators that consume bacteria and fungi and release the right forms of nutrients for your plants.*

QUESTION 1-7: *Do I need to feed any plants chemical fertilizers anymore?*

ANSWER 1-7: There is no need for inorganic fertilizers if soil life is healthy. But use an inorganic fertilizer even just once, and some of the soil life that would have helped nutrient cycling is destroyed. Organic fertilizers, such as compost, sea kelp, and humic acid, provide foods for the organisms as long as aerobic conditions remain. Do not overfeed. These organic fertilizers contain organic forms of nutrients that will be transformed by beneficial microbes into the correct forms for plants to take up.

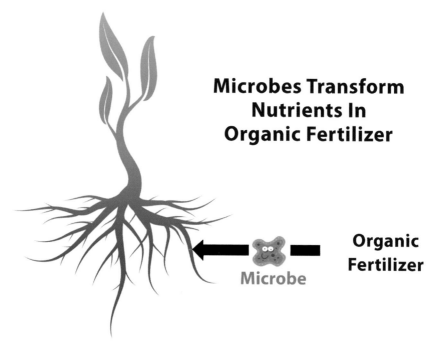

Microbes Transform Nutrients In Organic Fertilizer

Microbe

Organic Fertilizer

Microbes Transform Nutrients In Fertilizer: *Organic fertilizers contain organic forms of nutrients that will be transformed by beneficial microbes into the correct forms for plants to take up.*

QUESTION 1-8: *How is soil structure related to water and fertility?*

ANSWER 1-8: Good structure in the soil is required so that water can be held or can even move into soil. If water moves through the soil too fast, with no structure to hold the water in the soil, then many of the nutrients in your soil will be washed through and out of the soil. Without enough nutrients, your plant will suffer. This is a Goldilocks kind of thing: not too much too fast, not too little too slow, but just the right amount at the right speed—balance is the key.

Assessing
A Growing
System

In this chapter, we present a series of questions for you to ask yourself so you can evaluate the gardening products you use (or have used) in the last one to three years. A detailed explanation follows each question to help you understand how your current practices can interface with Gardening With Nature principles.

QUESTION 2-1: *Have I used pesticides, herbicides, or fungicides?*

ANSWER 2-1: If you answered yes, then you probably had problems in your garden, problems like diseases, weeds, and/or pests. You went to the garden store and found a product that said it could fix those problems. If you used toxic chemicals, then the problems you had were probably serious enough for you to spend money to try to alleviate them. Each time a toxic chemical is applied, though, residuals remain in the area to which they were applied. Ultimately, about 80 percent of the toxic chemicals applied to an unhealthy soil will move into streams, lakes, and rivers, and ultimately could contaminate your drinking water.

Use Of Toxic Chemicals: *If you used toxic chemicals, the problems you had were probably serious enough for you to spend money to try to alleviate them.*

QUESTION 2-2: *Did those chemicals fix my problems?*

ANSWER 2-2: Unfortunately, chemical products do not, and cannot, solve the underlying cause of the disease, weed, or insect pest problem. In fact, using toxic chemicals or inorganic salt fertilizers has probably made your initial problems even worse, including weed problems, poor plant growth, an excess need for water, wilting problems, fertility problems, and disease problems. The toxic chemicals you used may have indeed killed some of the disease-causing organisms, but these chemicals do not kill all the disease, weed, or insect pests.

The "Nuke-em" Approach: *The "kill anything that moves" approach is ultimately not sustainable because it doesn't fix the underlying cause. The "nuke-em" approach keeps killing the messenger (insect pests and fungal diseases are the messangers) but does nothing about the cause of the problem.*

The toxic chemical reduced a symptom of the problem but did not fix the problem. Insect pests and fungal diseases are messengers that nature sends to inform you that there is an underlying problem. Kill the first messenger, and nature will just send another one. The next messenger will be less friendly and have nastier consequences. The "kill anything that moves" approach is ultimately not sustainable because it doesn't fix the underlying cause. The "nuke-em" approach keeps killing the messenger but does nothing about the cause of the problem.

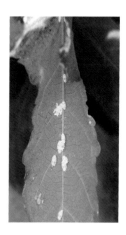

QUESTION 2-3: *Did any of the problems come back again?*

ANSWER 2-3: You will probably see the same problems coming back year after year. The use of toxic chemicals results in loss of soil life, making it impossible to Garden With Nature. Toxic chemicals kill things. How could something so toxic, that kills insects, weeds, birds, and even people (if they get too close), not also kill tiny organisms that are living in your soil and on your plants—bacteria, fungi, protozoa, nematodes, microarthropods, earthworms, roots, and so on?[1]

11

QUESTION 2-4: *How often do I apply chemicals to control problems?*

ANSWER 2-4: Recognize that constantly having to use toxic chemicals to control disease, pests, infertility, and water movement through the soil is a clear sign that something is terribly wrong with soil life. The damage that has been done cannot be fixed by using more toxic chemicals. On the other hand, if disease, pests, or weeds aren't routine issues— if they only turn up occasionally, every three or four years—then clearly the underlying problem isn't as far out of control. There's still something not right because the weeds, pests, or disease still show up, but fixing the situation will be much easier. With each use, and with each application of any toxic chemical, you grow further and further away from Gardening With Nature.

Having to constantly use toxic chemicals is a clear signal that something is terribly wrong.

QUESTION 2-5: *Did I use chemicals to combat weed problems?*

ANSWER 2-5: If you do nothing to your land for the next six months, what type of plants do you think will grow? If your answer is weeds, then pay attention to that messenger from nature. Weeds are nature's first step in returning health back to a soil that has been destroyed. If you use chemicals to get rid of those messenger weeds, what happens to nature's first step? You return once again to step zero. You just destroyed the beneficial life that was slowly starting to return to your soil and create a healthy growing system. So if you have weeds growing in your yard, you are at least on step 1, instead of at zero! "What?" you're saying. "Weeds in my yard? I don't want weeds in my yard!" So if you do not want a garden filled with weeds, you need to learn how to Garden With Nature. Once the whole system is established, then your weeds will naturally be under control. Got weeds? Then it's time to get working on returning more beneficial life to your soil to keep those weeds under control naturally so that you won't have to use toxic chemicals ever again.

Weeds are nature's first step in returning health back to a soil that has been destroyed.

QUESTION 2-6: *Have I used chemical fertilizers? When was the last time?*

ANSWER 2-6: If you have used any chemical synthetic fertilizers within the last few years, then many of the soil organisms that were present have been harmed or killed. In addition, residual toxic chemicals will have a continuing negative impact until they decompose. Only living organisms can decompose these toxic chemicals in a reasonable time frame. But if that life keeps getting killed before the job can be done, those toxic residuals will remain a problem.

QUESTION 2-7: *Do I know what chemical synthetic fertilizers are made from?*

ANSWER 2-7: All chemical synthetic fertilizers are salts. Table salt is one kind of salt, but there are thousands of other kinds of salts. Lime, gypsum, and ammonium nitrate are all examples of salts. Unless you use very minimal amounts of these salts (a teacup-sized amount over your entire lawn), these salts will steal water from everything in your lawn.

Use Of Toxic Chemicals: *Unless you use very minimal amounts of these salts (a teacup-sized amount over your entire lawn), these salts will steal water from everything in your lawn.*

QUESTION 2-8: *Can I use chemical fertilizers when I Garden With Nature?*

ANSWER 2-8: The salts in chemical synthetic fertilizers take water away from all life in the soil. The higher the salt concentration, the more difficult it is for soil life, including plants, to remain functional.

Chemical Fertilizers: *The salts in chemical synthetic fertilizers take water away from all life in the soil.*

QUESTION 2-9: *What will happen if I do use chemical fertilizers?*

ANSWER 2-9: The question of how much chemical fertilizer you can use without damage is different for each fertilizer. Immediate and serious negative impacts occur when the chemical inorganic fertilizer has salt levels above 75 parts per million (ppm). That translates into approximately 2 pounds of inorganic fertilizer on a typical suburban home lot or 200 pounds of fertilizer per acre. If more than 2 pounds of inorganic fertilizer are used at a time on a typical home lot, there will be significant and serious damage to soil life and all the functions they perform.

If more than 2 pounds of inorganic fertilizers are used at a time on a typical home lot, there will be significant and serious damage to soil life.

Step Three

Using Environmentally Friendly Gardening Products

In this chapter, we present a series of questions for you to ask yourself to evaluate the environmentally friendly gardening products you may find in gardening stores. A detailed explanation follows each question to help you understand how these products make practical contributions to Gardening With Nature.

QUESTION 3-1: *What gardening products will work best for Gardening With Nature?*

ANSWER 3-1: Some examples of gardening products that will work with nature are compost tea, sea kelp, humic acid, fish hydrolysate, mycorrhizal spores, compost, or worm castings. The products to look for are derived from an organic source.

| Compost Tea | Sea Kelp | Humic Acid | Mycorrhizae | Worm Castings |

Gardening Products That Work With Nature: *Examples of gardening products that work with nature are compost tea, sea kelp, humic acid, mycorrhizae, and worm castings.*

QUESTION 3-2: *What does **organic** mean?*

ANSWER 3-2: Organic means that the products were produced by organisms, without further processing with inorganic chemicals. Use of strong acids or bases or inorganic chemicals will leave chemical residues in the end product, which will harm or destroy any living organisms the chemicals contact.

QUESTION 3-3: *What does an **organically-allowed** seal mean?*

ANSWER 3-3: Even if a product says that it is organic, you must check that it has been allowed for organic production by a certifying agency. A seal and the name of the certifying agency are usually present on the container. Be careful of wording: products used for organic crops are not certified organic but rather are allowed for organic production by agencies that check the product for compliance with National Organic Program (NOP) standards. Nobody can stop a company from simply writing the word "organic" on its product container, but that is literally just an advertising gimmick, which may or may not help you in determining if the product will work in your Gardening With Nature growing environment.

Even if a product says it is organic you must check that it has been allowed or listed, or registered by a certifying agency.

QUESTION 3-4: *Are **all** organically-allowed products compatible with Gardening With Nature?*

ANSWER 3-4: Even if a product is allowed for organic production, it may not be compatible for Gardening With Nature. For example, some sea kelp may contain salt levels that are over 75 ppm if applied in quantities recommended by the manufacturer. Organically approved pesticides, from organophosphates to sulfur to insecticidal soap to neem oil to many organic herbs in high concentrations, do kill disease-causing organisms but at the same time also kill beneficial organisms.[2]

QUESTION 3-5: *How can I test to see if the salt levels in a product are too high?*

ANSWER 3-5: You can do your own testing to adjust electrical conductivity (EC) levels by changing the types, quantities, and feeding schedules of the nutrients you add. If the package says, for example, to use 20 ounces in 10 gallons of water, you can set up a small test. Twenty ounces in 10 gallons is the same as 2 ounces in 1 gallon (just remove the zero from both the ounces and the gallons). For your test, mix 2 ounces of the kelp in 1 gallon of water (be sure to remove the chlorine or chloramines in the water first, though). Then use an EC meter to test the salt levels.[3]

2 oz Kelp **+** **1 Gal Water**

Set up a small test for measuring EC levels.

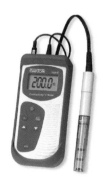

Use an EC meter to test the salt levels.

QUESTION 3-6: *What if the test shows that salt levels in a product are too high?*

ANSWER 3-6: If salt levels are over 100 micro-siemens per centimeter (µS/cm), or about 75 ppm, then dilute the kelp even more, for example, by mixing 1 ounce of kelp in 1 gallon of water or 1 ounce of kelp in 2 gallons of water (instead of 2 ounces, as suggested in Question 3-5). Keep diluting until the EC reading is less than 100 µS/cm. Then use the kelp at that dilution rate for spraying the product on your plants, as a soil drench, or for incorporation into your hydro system.

Before　　　　　　　　　　　　**After**

Bougainvilla Plant Before And After Using Gardening With Nature Products: *Laurie Keit from Seasonal Celebrations in Belmont, California applied Gardening With Nature products to the plant shown in the photo on the left. The photo on the right shows the results after two applications in three months. Dry and liquid products were used. (Photo courtesy of Laurie Keit, Seasonal Celebrations.)*

Before　　　　　　　　　　　　**After**

Apple Tree Before And After Using Gardening With Nature Products: *Laurie Keit from Seasonal Celebrations in Belmont, California applied Gardening With Nature products to the apple tree shown in the photo on the left. The photo on the right shows the results after five applications over a six-month period. (Photo courtesy of Laurie Keit, Seasonal Celebrations.)*

Step Four

Determining
A Plants'
Health

In this chapter, we present a series of questions for you to ask yourself to evaluate the health of the plants in your yard. A detailed explanation follows each question to help you understand how Gardening With Nature can help restore your plants to health.

QUESTION 4-1: *What does a healthy plant look like?*

ANSWER 4-1: During the growing season, healthy plants are green and growing, not yellowed with purplish veins, burned edges, or brown or curled leaves. They have the desired shape and are not leggy or spindly. They do not fall over. Healthy plants set fruit or seed at the usual time, and that fruit or seed develops in a normal fashion. Healthy plants have no symptoms of virus or disease attack, do not attract pest insects, and are not attacked by root-feeding insects or nematodes. Healthy plants contain properly balanced nutrient levels; they are a normal green color (check native plant Web sites for natural color).

QUESTION 4-2: *What are the symptoms of unhealthy plants?*

ANSWER 4-2: Disease, pests, and weeds will make an appearance if nutrients are not being taken up by the plant at the rates and in the proper balances that the plant requires. If the plant is experiencing difficulty, then some other plant will be able to outcompete it for sunlight, root space, and nutrients. Abnormal growth is typical when the plant is not healthy.

Diseases, Pests, And Weeds: *Disease, pests, and weeds will make an appearance if nutrients are not being taken up by the plant at the rates and in the proper balances that the plant requires.*

QUESTION 4-3: *What if my plants' leaves are yellow and the plants are losing leaves?*

ANSWER 4-3: Prematurely yellowed, veined, spotted, or wilted plants indicate that the plant is being forced to steal nutrients from the older parts of the plant to maintain current production. Clearly the plant is not healthy if it has to do this. It is not normal for healthy plants to yellow or lose leaves. This indicates a lack of the predators in the soil that do the job of maintaining the levels of plant-available nutrients.

QUESTION 4-4: *Are there any tests for nutrient deficiency?*

ANSWER 4-4: Visual observation is the most rapid and least expensive way to learn whether the plant is getting the nutrients it needs in proper balance. To get quantitative data on nutrient concentrations, a plant tissue test should be done. Despite what chemical fertilizer salesmen might try to convince you of, the facts are that soil chemistry tests do not give information on what will end up in the plant. Measuring soluble or exchangeable nutrient concentrations in the soil does not predict what the plant has or will take up. The best test to predict nutrient deficiencies is to assess the organisms in the soil. The organisms are what change any nutrient from a non-plant-available form into a plant-available form. You need to know that this organism workforce is present and doing its job. Therefore it is best to measure the organisms in the soil to know if nutrient cycling is even possible.

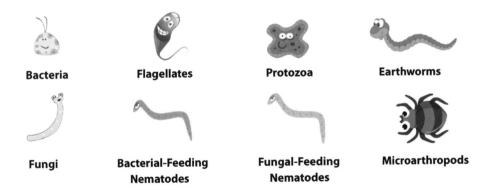

Bacteria   **Flagellates**   **Protozoa**   **Earthworms**

Fungi   **Bacterial-Feeding Nematodes**   **Fungal-Feeding Nematodes**   **Microarthropods**

The best test to predict nutrient deficiencies is to assess the organisms in the soil.

QUESTION 4-5: *What is a disease-causing organism? What is a pest?*

ANSWER 4-5: Plant pathogens, or disease organisms, usually decompose living tissue while the plant is still alive. Eventually the whole plant will be harmed and likely die. Pests and parasites, on the other hand, consume a part of the plant and eventually consume enough plant material that production is reduced or harmed beyond what humans can tolerate. Examples are aphids on roses, grubs on tomatoes, or worms in apples. Why would a toxic chemical, whether organic or not, that kills disease organisms not also kill beneficial microbes? No matter what type of mechanism is used, a pesticide that kills bad guys also affects good guys. No mechanism for killing disease organisms is so specific that it only kills one species of organism and no others.

Examples of pests are aphids on roses and worms in apples.

QUESTION 4-6: *How do plants resist disease or pests?*

ANSWER 4-6: The key to resisting disease or pests is to have a healthy root system, going as deep as the physiology of the plant can manage. If the roots go deep into the soil, then the roots have more access to water and nutrients. If the plant is able to get all the nutrients it needs, easily and without stress, then the plant will be able to resist all but the most overwhelming of disease or pest attacks.

Step Five

Preparing Soil

In this chapter, we present a series of questions for you to ask yourself when you are preparing soil for planting in your yard. A detailed explanation follows each question to help you understand how Gardening With Nature can help with soil preparation.

Soil Composition: *The goal is to achieve a soil composition with a minimum of 3 to 5 percent organic matter, with a full, properly balanced set of organisms.*

QUESTION 5-1: *How do I prepare my soil for new plantings?*

ANSWER 5-1: The goal is to achieve a soil composition with a minimum of 3 to 5 percent organic matter, with a full, properly balanced set of organisms. With a fully functioning food web, excellent soil structure can be built, nutrient cycling will be rapid enough, and the nutrients will be in the right places to support a healthy plant. If soil structure has been built and all the organisms needed are present, then adequate water will be held through most seasons.

QUESTION 5-2: *How much organic matter should be in my soil?*

ANSWER 5-2: First you need to understand a few facts about humic acids, which are a specific type of organic matter crucial to Gardening With Nature. Humic acids are a specific type of organic matter. All organisms in soil contribute to humic acid formation, but fungi are probably the most important in good humus formation. While all types of organic matter can chemically bind, or tie up, any kind of salt or toxic material, humic acids are notable for having the greatest ability to rapidly bind any salt in any solution. Thus, when water quality is questionable, addition of humic acid is one way to deal with the problem. Note, however, that the actual compound has not vanished; rather it is just not extractable any longer using common soil-testing equipment.

Without soil organisms to incorporate the compounds into the chemical structure of an organic compound, salts bound to a humic acid will be released in about two weeks' time and again become a problem for your plants. Remember that salt problems cause browning at the edges of leaves; an odd curling, bubbling appearance to leaves; and leaf wilting. If your response to these symptoms is to water more, typically you just end up waterlogging your soil and causing anaerobic conditions to develop.

Salt Problems: *Salt problems cause an odd curling, browning at the edges of leaves, and leaf wilting.*

To sustain soil organisms in an active condition to protect your plants, soil needs to contain organic matter at levels above 3 percent or humus above 2 percent, more or less. If organic matter reaches higher levels, just make sure that the organisms that are needed to build soil structure are there too. So if you have high organic matter with no biology present, then structure will not be built. There will be no passageways for water or air to move into or through the soil, and an anaerobic mess can develop rapidly. Anaerobic organisms that become active in these waterlogged environments will then produce a habitat that is deadly to plant roots. To eliminate anaerobic conditions, the soil must be completely aerated and aerobic organisms added.

 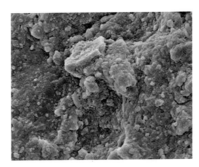

Aerobic soil with air and water passageways

Anaerobic soil with <u>NO</u> air and water passageways

QUESTION 5-3: *What kind of compost should I use?*

ANSWER 5-3: Correctly made, aerobic compost with the full diversity of organisms that are needed by the plant will provide the source of the foods, nutrients, and organisms. The book *Edible Forest Gardens* by David Jacke contains a list of about 300 plants and the normal balances of soil life for those plants.

Correctly Made Aerobic Compost: *Correctly made, aerobic compost with the full diversity of organisms that are needed by the plant will provide the source of the foods, nutrients, and organisms.*

Be careful of compost made with feedlot manure. Manure can be fine, if it is from an organic farm or pasture-fed animals. But when animals are fed materials that contain a great deal of salt, are high in antibiotics, or are high in preservatives, then those materials may be in the manure. Making compost with good sets of organisms to benefit plants is really hard to do when starting with feedlot manure. Some feedlot manures have documented levels of 1,000 ppm or more of salt, which will prevent almost any plant-friendly organism from growing.

Manure can be fine, if it is from an organic farm or pasture-fed animals.

26

When in doubt about compost quality, ask for test results on salt levels (EC) or for documentation of the bacteria, fungi, protozoa, and nematodes observed in the manure. Protozoa, beneficial fungi, and earthworms can serve as your "canary in the coal mine": if the material lacks these organisms, be suspicious. If a compost maker won't give you these data, do not buy that material.

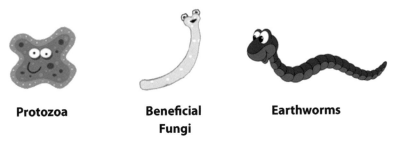

Protozoa   **Beneficial Fungi**   **Earthworms**

Protozoa, Beneficial Fungi, And Earthworms: *Protozoa, beneficial fungi, and earthworms can serve as your "canary in the coal mine": if the material lacks these organisms, be suspicious.*

QUESTION 5-4: *What kind of plant-growing environment is necessary for healthy plants?*

ANSWER 5-4: With good soil structure, plenty of food, and space for beneficial organisms to cycle nutrients, diseases and pests have no space, no food, and no way to gain a foothold on the plant. This habitat is built and maintained by beneficial organisms at the proper balance and level of activity.

This habitat is built and maintained by beneficial organisms at the proper balance and level of activity.

27

QUESTION 5-5: *How do I start creating a Gardening With Nature environment in my yard?*

ANSWER 5-5: Start using gardening products that work with nature and have the organisms needed to help your plants and that feed these beneficial organisms. Fertilizers, weeds, water, disease, and pests do not play major roles when Gardening With Nature. An environment that sustains aerobic microbial life provides food and nutrients for your plants. Bacteria and fungi hold or retain minerals, while protozoa, beneficial nematodes, and microarthropods change nutrients from forms that plants can't use into plant-available forms. The majority of these interactions occur in the root zone so the plant gets the immediate benefit of these interactions.

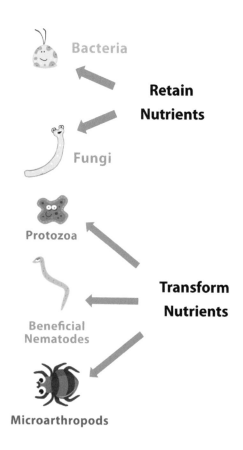

QUESTION 5-6: *Do I really have to add microbes? Can't I just use really good organic products?*

ANSWER 5-6: Without the full set of microbes in your growing system, you could use the best organic products available on the market but not achieve any of the benefits you want. This is the reason many people trying to switch to organic farming are not successful. The addition of the full set of beneficial microbes to the system is critical.

Beneficial Microbes Critical: *The addition of the full set of beneficial microbes to the system is critical.*

28

How does nature achieve balance in the natural growing world?

QUESTION 5-7: *How does nature achieve balance in the natural growing world?*

ANSWER 5-7: As any piece of land goes through succession (bare soil to weeds to grasses to shrubs to trees), the balance of organisms in the food web in the soil builds as well, from just bacteria to bacteria and fungi; to bacteria, fungi, and protozoa; to more and more kinds and types of organisms and species. As life builds in diversity and function, soil is built from not very productive to increasingly productive. Soil structure is built deeper and deeper, increasing the depth to which roots can go, increasing the rate of nutrient cycling, and increasing the potential production of the plant community. Watching that process of building is amazing, but it gives clues about how to manage your land if you want to stop the process of succession at the stage of development that selects for the plants you want to have.

Plant Succession

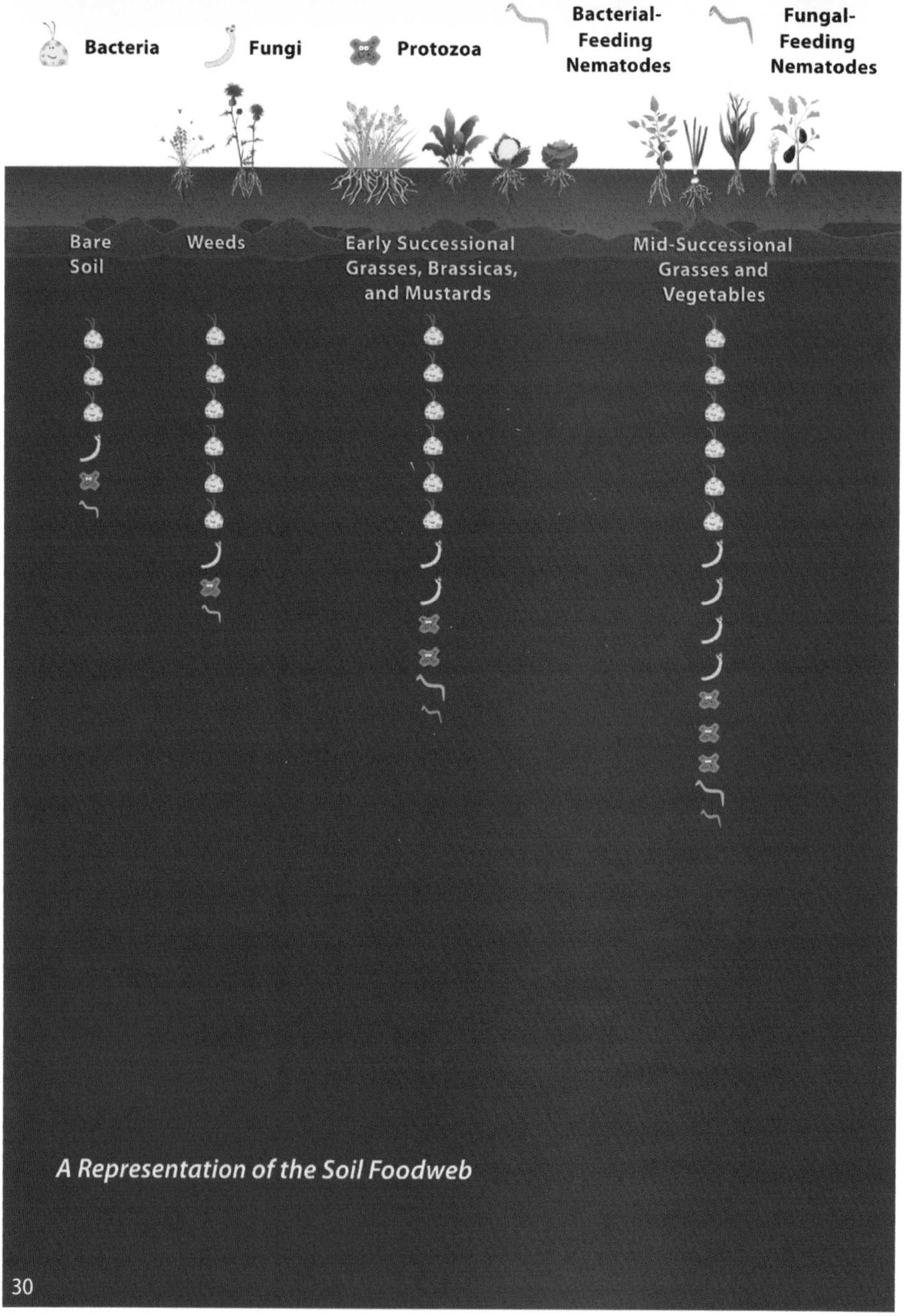

Bacteria   Fungi   Protozoa

Some Bacterial-Feeding Nematodes

More Bacterial-Feeding Nematodes

Some Fungal-Feeding Nematodes

More Fungal-Feeding Nematodes

Bare Soil

Weeds

Early Successional Grasses, Brassicas, and Mustards

Mid-Successional Grasses and Vegetables

A Representation of the Soil Foodweb

Some Predatory Nematodes

Some Microarthropods

More Predatory Nematodes

More Microarthropods

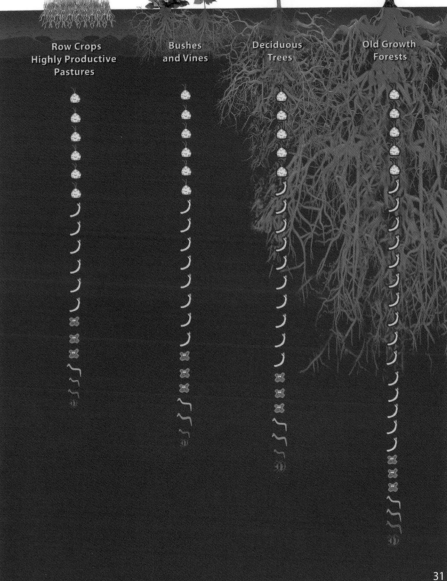

Row Crops Highly Productive Pastures

Bushes and Vines

Deciduous Trees

Old Growth Forests

QUESTION 5-8: *Will I ever have to rebalance my growing environment once it is established?*

ANSWER 5-8: Once your plants are feeding the life in the soil, and life in the soil is sustaining your plants (watch your plants to make sure things are going right), you should not have to apply your soil organisms again, unless some drastic disturbance occurs.

Watch your plants to make sure things are going right.

Apply Good Compost, Extract, Or Tea: *Apply to replenish what may have been lost. Remember that a thick layer of compost should not be placed on the stem of a plant because airflow to the bark (or stem) should never be restricted.*

Be aware of what harms beneficial organisms, and when in doubt of whether a flood, severe drought, or potential pesticide drift might have harmed your organisms, either test to make sure of what happened or apply good compost, extract, or tea to replenish what may have been lost. Remember that a thick layer of compost should not be placed on the stem of a plant because airflow to the bark (or stem) should never be restricted.

Step Six

Planting
and
Transplanting

QUESTION 6-1: *How do I plant new flowers, shrubs, and trees?*

ANSWER 6-1: When planting in a hole or in the pot, gradually mix about a fifty-fifty ratio of the soil that was taken out with high-quality compost. Vary the compost concentration so that nearly straight soil is near the edges of the hole or pot and increase the amount of compost until the area where the root ball or roots sit is a fifty-fifty mix, or maybe a little higher in compost.

Apply Good Compost, Compost Tea, Or Extract:
Vary the compost concentration so that nearly straight soil is near the edges of the hole or pot, and increase the amount of compost until the area where the root ball or roots sit is a fifty-fifty mix or maybe a little higher in compost.

QUESTION 6-2: *How does mixing compost and soil help roots grow?*

ANSWER 6-2: When compost with good life in it is mixed into soil with not so great sets of organisms, then good soil structure should develop. As structure is built and as nutrient cycling begins to occur normally, roots will be encouraged to grow deeper into the soil. The factors that caused roots to refuse to cross the "clay pot sides" of the potting hole will be alleviated. Roots cannot grow into hard, compacted, low-oxygen soil. This low-oxygen environment is where anaerobic processes produce materials that will kill the roots and encourage disease and pest organisms.

As structure is built and as nutrient cycling begins to occur normally, roots will be encouraged to grow deeper into the soil.

QUESTION 6-3: *Should I feed my plants any food after transplanting?*

ANSWER 6-3: While the plant is recovering from transplanting, it would be a good idea to add a handful of food to the mix that will help beneficial fungi grow and establish around the root system of the plant. The amount isn't absolute, although if you know what is lacking, you can be more precise. In general, add about a handful of organic microbe food/nutrients, such as dried fish, kelp, fish flakes, ground oatmeal, bran, barley, or other grain material, to each 5 gallons of potting mix or planting soil.

Add a Handful Of Organic Microbe Food/Nutrients: *In general, add about a handful of organic microbe food/nutrients, such as dried fish, kelp, fish flakes, ground oatmeal, bran, barley, or other grain material, to each 5 gallons of potting mix or planting soil.*

QUESTION 6-4: *How should I care for the soil after transplanting?*

ANSWER 6-4: Make certain that you do not disturb the planting medium, or disturb it as little as possible, once the beneficial organisms are growing. Potting up plants requires some mixing, but once potted, avoid mixing and tilling as these practices will slice and crush many of the best organisms. Since the organisms build the hallways and passageways that allow air and water to move normally, any disruption that destroys the organisms will cause problems down the line with plant health—unless remediation is performed to offset the damage done.

Dip Bare Roots: *Dip bare roots in a mixture of mycorrhizal fungal spores and compost tea just before planting.*

QUESTION 6-5: *How should I prepare and plant seeds?*

ANSWER 6-5: Roll or soak seeds (about a fifteen-minute quick soak) in a mixture of mycorrhizal fungal spores and compost tea before planting. Dry the seeds if you aren't going to plant right away. Dip bare roots in a mixture of mycorrhizal fungal spores and compost tea (letting them soak for fifteen minutes is fine too) just before planting. You can also put the mycorrhizal fungal spores out in your planting furrows or holes and drench the soil in the planting hole with compost tea and other organic nutrients while planting.

QUESTION 6-6: *How do I add beneficial organisms when planting gardens, crops, lawns, or pastures?*

ANSWER 6-6: In gardens, cropping systems, and lawns or pastures, mix beneficial organisms into the soil or apply them to the soil surface, if needed.[4]

Mix beneficial organisms into the soil or apply them to the soil surface, if needed.

QUESTION 6-7: *What kind of balance of beneficial organisms do shrubs, perennial flowers, and herbs need?*

ANSWER 6-7: Shrubs, perennial flowers, and herbs are plants that need a wider array of species of beneficial fungi and some bacteria. Perennial plants in general all need their mycorrhizal fungal counterparts to colonize the roots and collect nutrients for the plant. Make sure as wide a diversity as possible of mycorrhizal spores are added to the soil right in the root zone.[5]

Bacteria

Fungi

Mycorrhizal Fungi

Shrubs, Perennials, Flowers, And Herbs: *Shrubs, perennial flowers, and herbs are plants that need a wider array of species of beneficial fungi and some bacteria. Perennial plants in general all need their mycorrhizal counterparts to colonize roots and collect nutrients for the plant.*

QUESTION 6-8: *What kind of balance of beneficial organisms do annual or biennial flowers need?*

ANSWER 6-8: Annual or biennial flowers need more bacteria than fungi. But remember that most of the time, our gardening and soil management has knocked out the fungi. To get the beneficial fungi back, most of the time, strongly fungal compost, tea, or extract and lots of fungal foods are required.[6]

Bacteria   **Fungi**

Annual Or Biennial Flowers: *Annual or biennial flowers need more bacteria than fungi. But our gardening and soil management has knocked out the fungi. So beneficial fungi need to be replaced.*

Potting Mix When Planting Annuals: *Generally, mix compost into the sterile potting material at rates between 1 and 10 percent by weight of the final material. If you have excellent compost, just use compost for the potting mix.*

QUESTION 6-9: *What do I use for a potting mix when planting annuals?*

ANSWER 6-9: When potting annual plants, the initial compost application is dependent on the potting material being used. If possible, get the seller of the potting mix to document the food web in the potting mix, or test it yourself. Generally, mix compost into the sterile potting material at rates between 1 and 10 percent by weight of the final material. If excellent compost, that is, balanced soil food web, is used, just use compost for the potting mix.

Once the plants are potted, place a quarter to a half-inch of compost on the surface of the solid medium. Add liquid compost (compost extract or tea) to the watering reservoir to maintain the needed diversity of organisms. Always use the highest quality organic products with the balances of food webs of organisms needed by your plant.

Add compost extract or compost tea to the watering reservoir to maintain the needed diversity of organisms.

Step Seven

Feeding Plants

QUESTION 7-1: *How often should I spray organic nutrients and microbes on plants?*

ANSWER 7-1: Until such time as the proper balance of microorganisms is established, improvement of the biology needs to be continued. Once correct balance is achieved, the plant should maintain that balance. Compost, in solid or liquid form (compost extract or teas), should be applied at monthly intervals while the plant is growing. Once the balance of microorganisms has been established and the plants are showing a return to health, the soil becomes open and soft again and applications can be reduced to once a year.

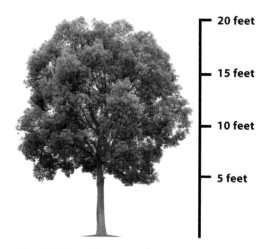

20 feet

15 feet

10 feet

5 feet

Use 5 Gallons Of Compost Tea Per Acre: *For foliar applications, use 5 gallons of top-notch, properly made, aerobic, highly microbial compost tea per acre for every 5 feet of tree height of the canopy.*

QUESTION 7-2: *How much organic nutrient should I give my trees?*

ANSWER 7-2: For foliar applications, use 5 gallons of top-notch, properly made, aerobic, highly microbial compost tea per acre for every 5 feet of tree height of the canopy. If the compost does not have good levels of biology, then you may need to use 10 gallons, or 50, or even 100. The amount of compost or tea needed is strictly dependent on the biology in the compost or tea.

QUESTION 7-3: *Will I be able to prevent and control diseases on my plants?*

ANSWER 7-3: If 70 to 100 percent of your plant surface is covered with beneficial microbes, then disease organisms will be outcompeted for food and space. While only a few scientific papers have been published about compost tea prevention and suppression of diseases, observations by growers that enhancing biology results in disease control are extensive. Don't forget to spray microbes on your plant stems too!

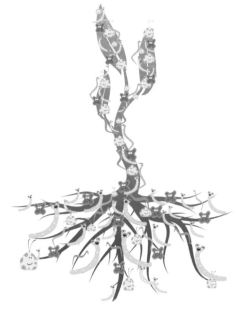

70-100 Percent Of The Plant Covered With Beneficial Microbes: *If 70-100 percent of your plant surface is covered with beneficial microbes, then disease organisms will be outcompeted for food and space.*

Keep An Eye On Your Plants: *Keep an eye on your plants for any evidence of something disturbing them, even if you have perfect growing conditions.*

QUESTION 7-4: *If I have perfect growing conditions, what more do I need to do?*

ANSWER 7-4: If you have established microbial life in your soil, if you have improved organic matter concentrations to 5 percent, and if no environmental disturbance occurs (such as pesticide drift, pesticide residues in water, high salts, or heavy metals in water), then your plants will obtain all the nutrients they need from the soil, resulting in healthy plant growth. Still, keep an eye on your plants for any evidence of something disturbing them.

The amount of compost or tea needed is strictly dependent on the biology in the compost or tea.

Air Pollution: *Given ongoing air pollution from so many sources, it may be necessary to plan on a compost application to the soil surface once or twice a year, and monthly applications of compost tea through the growing season.*

QUESTION 7-5: *If I do not have perfect growing conditions, what do I need to do?*

ANSWER 7-5: In our modern world, many insults and injuries to the environment are somewhat out of your control. Right now, most people need to start by adding all the microbes to get natural nutrient cycling processes going again. Reestablishment of the normal populations of organisms to plant surfaces is necessary as well. Given ongoing air pollution from so many sources, it may be necessary to plan on a compost application to the soil surface once or twice a year and monthly applications of compost tea to the plants' above ground surfaces through the growing season, depending on disturbances and air pollution contamination.

QUESTION 7-6: *How much nutrient do I need to add if I am also using compost teas?*

ANSWER 7-6: When you use organic nutrients in conjunction with compost teas, you can usually reduce the recommended amount of inorganic fertilizers by at least half in the first year, and then by another half in the second year, by which time, no inorganic fertilizers will be needed, provided that proper soil life is maintained.

You can usually reduce the recommended amount of inorganic fertilizer by at least half in the first year, and then by another half in the second year.

There is a vast reservoir of nutrients in sand, silt, clay, rocks, pebbles, and organic matter.

QUESTION 7-7: *Do I need to add any inorganic synthetic chemicals?*

ANSWER 7-7: As the microbes become established, inorganic nutrient additions are no longer needed. The reason people have said in the past that harvesting plants mines out nutrients is because they haven't paid attention to anything except the soluble forms of nutrients and have ignored the vast amounts of nutrients not in soluble forms in soil. As in any natural system, nutrients are constantly cycling into all the different forms and pools of nutrients in soil. There is a vast reservoir of nutrients in sand, silt, clay, rocks, pebbles, and organic matter. They are not soluble forms of nutrients, but if the organisms in your soil include bacteria, fungi, protozoa, nematodes, and microarthropods in proper balance for the plant, then compost with good biology is all you need to keep plants healthy.

QUESTION 7-8: *How much compost or liquid compost should be used?*

ANSWER 7-8: Enough should be used to reestablish the organisms that are needed and to get them active and functioning. Typically, one ton of good compost per acre will reestablish organisms, but then testing is needed to determine whether they survived the addition process.[7]

QUESTION 7-9: *Should I till the compost in?*

ANSWER 7-9: You should till if, and only if, there is severe compaction and there is no other way to get the organisms to chew their way into the compaction layer in a reasonable length of time. If there is a good litter layer and the soil surface is not compacted, then there should be no reason to till.[8]

QUESTION 7-10: *How can I use compost I made last year?*

ANSWER 7-10: Yes, but you may have to improve it. To improve mulch that has no decent biology, or to revive compost or worm castings that have dried out or have been sitting for a long time without adequate moisture, add a small amount of good compost. If the compost has just been sitting with adequate moisture, add foods to wake up the beneficial organisms. This will allow nutrient cycling to increase through microbial action.

Litter Layer: *If there is a good litter layer and the soil surface is not compacted, then there should be no reason to till.*

Mulch: *To improve mulch that has no decent biology or to revive compost or worm castings that have dried out or have been sitting for a long time without adequate moisture, add a small amount of good compost.*

QUESTION 7-11: *Can I add nutrients to my compost or mulch?*

ANSWER 7-11: Yes. For example, if the plan was to apply 100 pounds of humic acid directly to your soil, you could reduce that amount to 10 pounds if a good diversity of microorganisms was previously applied to a humic acid–compost mix. Once the organisms have awakened and are functioning, apply humic acid to the soil surface or lightly mix it into the soil that needs resuscitation. How much is needed really depends on whether the organisms start working after that food is added. A dusting of humic acid or a gallon of liquid humic per acre is usually adequate if the biology is present and just needs a wake-up call.

QUESTION 7-12: *Do I need to add inorganic synthetic chemical nutrients?*

ANSWER 7-12: If the diversity of organisms has not been harmed, if organic matter is present, and if sand, silt, clay, or other mineral nutrients are present, then there is no reason to add inorganic nutrients. So how much inorganic nutrient should you add to your growing medium? None. Instead you need the correct sets of organisms. They need to be fed. Three percent organic matter or more will allow the organisms to have the food they need to function without you adding more food. More is better, as long as the organisms are working and building structure in that organic matter so oxygen can move easily into the root zone.

QUESTION 7-13: *Do I need to send my growing medium to be tested for chemical analysis of N-P-K?*

ANSWER 7-13: People have often been convinced that their planting materials have no nutrients at all, based on chemical testing that they have done. Please do not fall for that sales pitch. Be aware that only a miniscule amount of the total nutrients (e.g., N-P-K) actually present in your soil or soilless media are reported on a soil chemistry test. Chemical analyses of the soluble (they are dissolved in soil water) pool of nutrients assess only a small fraction of what is present in soil. In a decent soil with 3 percent or so organic matter, the soluble forms of any nutrient you might want to look at are usually less than 0.1 to 1 percent of the total of that nutrient present.

Overtillage: *All beneficial life in the soil is killed by overtillage and overuse of pesticides and herbicides.*

Why would a company that sells inorganic fertilizers focus only on the soluble forms? Well, that is what plants take up, and if all the beneficial life in the soil is killed by overtillage and overuse of pesticides and herbicides, and all the food for the organisms is gone (burned, raked off, etc.), then the way nature has to convert the non-plant-available forms into plant-available forms is no longer present. So if you are planting in dirt with no beneficial life, then nutrient cycling will not take place. In the absence of nutrient cycling, you have to add the nutrients in the form the plant needs because you have taken away what normally cycles those nutrients. But soluble nutrients leach out of the soil. And with no life in the soil to grab those nutrients before they leave, those nutrients will destroy water quality everywhere downstream.

Soluble nutrients leach out of the soil. With no life in the soil to grab nutrients before they leave, those nutrients will destroy water quality everywhere downstream.

We don't need to know the specific name of each organism present, just that there are adequate amounts.

QUESTION 7-14: *How many kinds of microorganisms do I need?*

ANSWER 7-14: Microorganisms transform nutrients from plant-unavailable forms into plant-available forms. Different nutrients are transformed by different species of microbes. Different conditions (temperature, moisture amount, oxygen concentration, mineral nutrient and food concentrations, types of food, etc.) will select for the growth of different organisms. You don't need to know the specific name of each organism present; you just need to know that there are adequate amounts of each type of organism. Each species performs different functions given the conditions, which are constantly changing. But all the jobs need to get done, no matter what the environmental conditions. Soil must have an incredible diversity of all these different organism groups. Where can you find, or make, the organism mix that is best for your plants? The answer is compost: properly made, aerobic compost. Thermal or worm, they can both do the job.

Soil must have an incredible diversity of all these different organism groups.

47

Come forth into the light of things.
Let nature be your teacher. ~ William Wordsworth

Step Eight

Fixing Problems

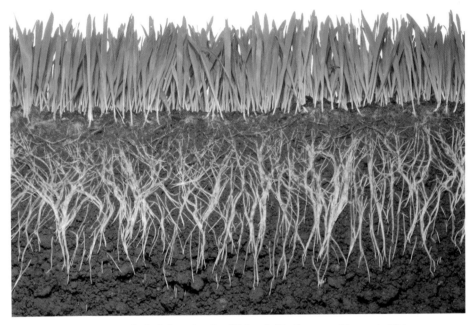

Organisms In Soil: *Organisms in soil help to build soil structure. Destroy the life in the soil, and soil structure cannot be maintained — with no structure, plants suffer.*

QUESTION 8-1: *If I have poor soil, do these microbes help?*

ANSWER 8-1: All the organisms in soil help to build soil structure so that air and water can move deep into the soil. All our crop species, from broccoli to bananas, mustards to mango, require air to keep root systems alive. Destroy the life in the soil, and soil structure cannot be maintained—and without any structure, plants suffer.

Tillage: *One tillage event a year can be recovered from if a healthy soil is close by. But constant and unremitting tillage will rapidly destroy all the beneficial life in the soil, leaving only compaction, disease, pests, and sick root systems.*

QUESTION 8-2: *Does tilling my soil affect soil structure or the organisms?*

ANSWER 8-2: Tillage of any kind destroys this structure built by soil life and, of course, crushes the organisms that built and live in the soil that was tilled. One tillage event a year can be recovered from, if a healthy soil is close by and the organisms in that healthy place will move back into the disturbed area. But constant and unremitting tillage will rapidly destroy all the beneficial life in the soil, leaving only compaction, disease, pests, and sick root systems.

QUESTION 8-3: *What happens when my soil is compacted?*

ANSWER 8-3: If compaction occurs, then water collects at the top of the compaction layer and puddles in the soil. Because oxygen does not move well at all through water, the conditions that select for diseases and pests will occur, and your plants' roots will suffer greater disease incidence and might even die, if things are bad enough.

Compaction: *If compaction occurs, then water collects at the top of the compaction layer and puddles in the soil.*

Balancing The Soil Environment: *By balancing the soil environment and rejuvenating soil structure, vegetables, row crops, healthy pasture, orchards, and forests can be grown sustainably.*

QUESTION 8-4: *What happens when my plants can't get nutrients because my soil is compacted?*

ANSWER 8-4: Once plants can no longer obtain nutrients or water from the soil, they are stressed and sick. As anaerobic bacteria become the predominant organism living in the soil, then the conditions are perfect for weeds. The addition of beneficial organisms can start to alter conditions so weeds no longer rule. By balancing the soil environment and rejuvenating soil structure, vegetables, row crops, healthy pasture, orchards, and forests can be grown sustainably.

The addition of beneficial organisms can start to alter conditions so weeds no longer rule.

Watch Your Plants: *If any problems (pests, disease, yellowing, spindly plants, etc.) are seen, start with compost tea on the foliage and drenched around the plant on the soil.*

QUESTION 8-5: *What if I see problems with my plants?*

ANSWER 8-5: Watch your plants. If any problems (pests, disease, yellowing, spindly plants, etc.) are seen, start with compost tea on the foliage (but first check to make sure the life needed is in the tea) and drench the soil around the plant. Pests should stop attacking the plant within a few hours, and certainly within three days. Disease symptoms should reverse within an eight- to twenty-four-hour period.

Observe the plant and make sure stress symptoms reverse.

Observe the plant and make sure stress symptoms reverse. If the problem still persists, make sure to assess the organisms in the compost and tea. If tea doesn't work, most likely the organisms were not actually in the compost or did not make it to the plant. If the problem does not resolve, then there are certain types of biocontrol organisms that might be added to compost teas for specific problems. Talk to an expert about which biocontrol organism to use.

When beneficial organisms aren't fed and there is no organic matter in the soil or soilless media, then nothing can protect roots, and that's the time that disease and pests will attack. When these problems are evident, it's time to add good compost or liquid forms of good compost again. This will rapidly add beneficial organisms and the foods to feed the beneficial organisms, so the problems are remedied immediately. Make sure the biology gets balanced correctly in the soil to start with and that life is maintained.

The plant will tell you eventually if something goes wrong, but by the time the plant is showing symptoms, it will be a race to see if the plant is going to live. Will you be able to reverse the stress before the plant dies? It is much better to deal with plants in a way to make sure the place they are growing is healthy and matches the plants' needs, and the plants are never stressed. That means monitoring the life in your soil and keeping an eye on the things that healthy soil life does for the soil, such as good structure, good smell, deep roots, and lots of organisms.

Balance The Biology: *Make sure the biology gets balanced correctly in the soil to start with and that life is maintained.*

QUESTION 8-6: *How can I fix nutrient deficiencies?*

ANSWER 8-6: Make certain that the full diversity of protozoa, beneficial nematodes, and microarthropods is present and functioning. Most likely you will need to add compost or a water extract from compost that has these mechanisms.

QUESTION 8-7: *What should I do if the soil for my plants gets out of balance?*

ANSWER 8-7: The basic answer is to add the right organisms back again, in the soil where the roots are growing. Now, once a plant is growing, digging up the roots to apply the right organisms isn't a good idea, so exactly how you apply the organisms depends a bit on the system the plant is in.

Put tea into the watering system if soil around the plant still has structure.

As long as the soil around the plant still has structure, so the water moves into the ground easily, then simply putting the tea into the watering system will work fine.

But check the soil for compaction. If it takes serious effort to push a metal rod into the soil, there's a problem. When soil is moist, compaction is usually less of a problem, but as soil dries, that compaction layer will be more noticeable.

To deal with roots where compaction has happened, try the following. Make five or six holes (angle each hole slightly toward the plant, if possible) in the ground in a circle around the plant, usually about halfway between the drip line and the stem of the plant. The size of the hole depends on the size of the plant. With small plants, the holes would only be an inch or so, deep, with a small diameter, but with a big tree, they should be a

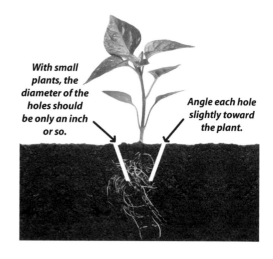

With small plants, the diameter of the holes should be only an inch or so.

Angle each hole slightly toward the plant.

A Big Tree: *Angle each hole slightly toward the plant, if possible. With a big tree, a foot or two depth and up to 2 to 3 inches in diameter for the holes is ideal.*

foot or two deep, and up to 2 to 3 inches in diameter is ideal. Drench the open holes with a good compost tea. Don't add foods to this tea because too many organisms growing in deep holes might not be a good idea. Too rapid bacterial or fungal growth, once the hole is filled with compost, could cause a lack of oxygen. If mycorrhizal fungi are needed on the roots, put mycorrhizal spores into the tea. Fill the holes with a mix of 70 percent compost containing as high a beneficial fungal component as possible and something that makes the compost easy to fill into the hole, such as sand, pea gravel, or vermiculite.

Mycorrhizal Fungi Spores: *If mycorrhizal fungi are needed on the roots, put mycorrhizal spores into the tea.*

Put one ring of five to six holes halfway between the drip line and the trunk and another set of six to ten holes out at the drip line.

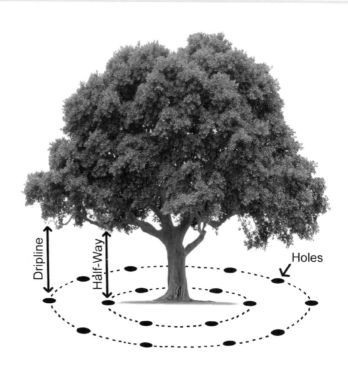

QUESTION 8-8: *What should I do if the soil for my trees gets out of balance?*

ANSWER 8-8: If trees are not doing well, do the same as in Answer 8-7, putting the holes as deep as you can drill, preferably down to below any compaction layer. More than one ring of holes should be made: put one ring of five to six holes halfway between the drip line and the trunk, and another set of six to ten holes out at the drip line, if the tree is big enough to have that extensive a root system.

Toxic Chemicals

QUESTION 8-9: *What should I do if toxic chemicals have been used and I have problems?*

ANSWER 8-9: If toxic chemicals have been used on healthy soil, beneficial organisms have been reduced. We are quite lucky, though, that the remedy is simple: replace the beneficial microbes that were killed by applying properly made aerobic compost, compost extract, or compost tea. Apply one of these products until the problem (diseases, pests, lack of fertility, weeds) subsides. You can send samples of soil or water to testing facilities for microbiological analysis to see if the organisms have been established, or you can get a microscope and test your own samples, if you get the proper training to identify the major groups of organisms.[9]

QUESTION 8-10: *What happens to the toxic residuals from pesticides and inorganic fertilizers?*

ANSWER 8-10: Finding the right species of microorganisms, and the conditions those species need to convince them to decompose toxic residuals from pesticides and inorganic fertilizers, can be tricky. Since pesticides and inorganic fertilizers kill the very organisms that do decomposition, it is most likely the case that the organisms are going to have to be added back into the place with the toxics, along with some modification of the system to make things better for the organisms. It's much better to never saddle yourself with this problem, but if it happens, getting some expert help to deal with the specifics of the situation is likely the best idea.

Pesticides And Inorganic Fertilizers: *Pesticides and inorganic fertilizers kill the very organisms that do decomposition.*

QUESTION 8-11: *Can beneficial organisms help with degrading toxic residuals?*

ANSWER 8-11: Aerobic conditions are required so that these beneficial organisms can survive and process the harmful materials. This means not only that the specific microbes that decompose these toxic chemicals must be present but that the entire set of nutrient-cycling, disease-suppressing organisms normally found in growing environments must be present and functioning. This entire food web is necessary to build structure and allow oxygen and water to move normally through the system.[10]

QUESTION 8-12: *How many times do I need to apply beneficial organisms to eliminate the problems?*

ANSWER 8-12: In most cases, the normal regime of establishing proper life in the soil also deals with any toxic residue problem. Sometimes addition of some special food resources or particular species of organisms might speed recovery, but this is rare.

Additional Applications: *After each time a neighbor applies a toxic chemical that moves into your space, another application of beneficial organisms will be needed.*

Even more rare is the case where it seems that the organisms just die as soon as they are applied, and you just can't get any benefit from putting out compost or tea. These exceptional cases indicate a serious toxic residue, and investigation into the problem is needed. An expert will be needed to deal with the severe toxicity indicated when you just can't establish life in your soil.

There are environmental insults that have to be considered too, such as a neighbor who won't give up spraying pesticide on windy days or spreading toxic powder that drifts into your yard. After each time the neighbor applies a toxic chemical that moves into your space, another application of beneficial organisms will be needed. But most neighbors see you working less, not using toxic materials, and with equally good or better looking plants, and pretty soon you are helping them become sustainable.

Sometimes neighbors won't give up spraying pesticide on windy days or spreading toxic powder that drifts into your yard.

Working Less: *Most neighbors will see you working less, not using toxic materials, and with equally good or better looking plants, and pretty soon you are helping them become sustainable.*

QUESTION 8-13: *How fast will I see results after applying beneficial organisms?*

ANSWER 8-13: The time it will take to fix a sick situation depends on just how bad things were to start. In addition, how fast recovery has to take place is also a factor. Overnight recovery will be expensive, but if you can work through a growing season, then the cost will be quite reasonable. If you have neighbors who won't respect your boundaries, then additional applications will be needed.

The least expensive way is to make and apply your own compost and tea. Of course, if you haven't killed all the beneficial life in your soil to begin with, the conversion to sustainable will be even easier. If you buy compost and tea from others, then the cost will be more than if you do it yourself. If others apply the materials, then the cost will go up and become comparable to what chemical applicator companies charge.

How easy will it be to establish the right set of organisms and to replenish the sources of food these organisms need to do their job? If a grower backslides and uses toxic chemicals to give a quick fix, the recovery process will take longer and will possibly never occur.[11]

QUESTION 8-14: *What is the least expensive way to implement this recovery process?*

ANSWER 8-14: If there is no need to hurry about the process of recovery, then in a few months, or possibly as long as a few years, there may be little more cost than learning to make good compost, learning about appropriate plants that combat weeds, and building a compost tea brewer.

Before

After

Landscape Border Before And After Using Gardening With Nature Products: *Laurie Keit from Seasonal Celebrations in Belmont, California applied Gardening Wth Nature products to the plants shown in the photo on the top. The photo on the bottom shows the results after dry and liquid products were applied. (Photo courtesy of Laurie Keit, Seasonal Celebrations.)*

Step Nine

Preparing
For The
Next Season

Residue Left In The Field, Garden, Or Lawn: *Use 20 gallons of good-quality compost tea per acre (less if the biology is excellent and in balance) as a soil drench each fall on the residues left in the field, garden, or lawn.*

QUESTION 9-1: *What should I do in the fall to prepare for winter?*

ANSWER 9-1: Use 20 gallons of good-quality compost tea per acre (less if the biology is excellent and in balance) as a soil drench each fall on the residues left in the field, garden, or lawn. If there were disease problems in the plants during the summer, the disease organisms growing on that diseased plant material have to be outcompeted, consumed, or otherwise prevented from having a place to live. Decomposition of the dead plant material will destroy the habitat that would otherwise let those disease organisms multiply through the winter.

Disease Problems In Summer: *If there were disease problems in the plants during the summer, the disease organisms growing on the diseased plant material have to be outcompeted, consumed, or otherwise prevented from having a place to live.*

Protect the soil surface through dormant periods by allowing snow to accumulate or by planting a green cover crop, or consider a permanent cover plant. Green cover crops tend to be grass species that often are hosts to the same diseases as the crop, and so the green cover crop has to be treated to get the biology right, just like the crop plant. It might be preferable to choose a plant that will not interfere with any farming operation but never leaves the soil bare.

Green Cover Crops: *Green cover crops tend to be grass species that often are hosts to the same diseases as the crop, and so the green cover crop has to be treated to get the biology right, just like the crop plant.*

Collect and compost the dead plant material.

Make sure that all dead plant material in hedgerows and under plants is decomposed and becomes soil during the dormant season. Collect and compost the dead plant material if it is a problem to maintain moisture to allow soil-making processes to occur in place.

What Should I Do In Spring To Prepare For Summer? *If lack of biology or proper balance requires, use 20 gallons of good-quality compost tea per acre as a soil drench in the spring.*

QUESTION 9-2: *What should I do in the spring to prepare for summer?*

ANSWER 9-2: If lack of biology or proper balance requires, use 20 gallons of good-quality compost tea per acre as a soil drench in the spring. Make sure the biology in the tea will replace the needed, missing biology in the soil. You should monitor the organisms to determine which organisms are missing, and whether the organisms are in the compost or in the tea and then start to balance correctly in the soil. If any group is low or missing, then additional applications are needed. If the amounts and balances of organisms are adequate, then no further additions are required.

In perennial systems, start applying compost tea as a foliar spray two weeks before buds break, whereas in annual plant systems, start applications of foliar teas at the first true leaf stage. Continue applying tea monthly to provide a plant-protective coating of beneficial microorganisms so they will be in place during known disease periods throughout the growing season.

Step Ten

Checking
The Quality
Of Water

**Send a
water sample
to a laboratory
for testing
for chlorine.**

QUESTION 10-1: *Does my water district use chlorine in my water?*

ANSWER 10-1: Is there a chlorine smell to your water? If you smoke, you might not be able to smell the chlorine, so you may need to ask your municipal water district if it uses chlorine. Alternatively, send a water sample to a laboratory for testing for chlorine (check your local water testing lab's Web site for directions on sampling and mailing).

**Check your
local water
testing lab's
web site for
directions on
sampling and
mailing.**

QUESTION 10-2: *Is there a way I can test my water for chlorine myself?*

ANSWER 10-2: Yes. Another possible approach is to use a pool chlorine testing kit.

QUESTION 10-3: *What can I do if there is chlorine in my water?*

ANSWER 10-3: If any chlorine is detected, filter your water because chlorine kills the organisms that you want to establish in any natural gardening system. A hose-end carbon-block filter will filter out most of the chlorine. You may need to put a filter at your water source (on the house tap) if you use automatic drip irrigation. Alternatively, chlorine is a gas, and it will, with adequate aeration, volatilize from the water.

QUESTION 10-4: *Does my water district use chloramine in my water?*

ANSWER 10-4: Ask your municipal water district if it uses chloramine in your water. Chloramine is a combination of chlorine and ammonia. Chloramine, like chlorine, is used to disinfect water supplies. Chloramine does not dissipate easily compared to chorine and is difficult to remove.

QUESTION 10-5: *What can I do if there is chloramine in my water?*

ANSWER 10-5: Activated carbon filters or reverse osmosis systems are needed to remove chloramine. Although recent developments have been made in this area, many emerging products have not been time tested, so talk with the manufacturer and run some tests if you are not sure that a product really works. Humus, which is most easily obtained from aerobic compost, can also remove chloramine. To obtain liquid humus, run water through dark brown–colored compost until the water is the color of a 70 percent cocoa chocolate bar.

A hose-end carbon-block filter will filter out most of the chlorine.

QUESTION 10-6: *How much salt is in my water?*

ANSWER 10-6: Ask your water district how much salt is in your water. If the EC of your water is above 10–12 µS/cm or 75 ppm salt, you will need to remove the salts with activated carbon and/or a reverse osmosis water filtration system, or you can complex the salts with humic acid. You can buy inexpensive EC meters at gardening and hydroponic stores or through the Internet (e.g., Pike Labs).

In nature we never see anything isolated, but everything in connection
with something else which is before it, beside it, under it, and over it.
~ Johann Wolfgang von Goethe

Notes

1. Chemical salesmen say that they have proof that their chemicals don't cause harm to beneficial organisms in soil or on plants, but look carefully at the work done. They use methods that cannot possibly show any damage and yet present that as proving that no harm was done. It's rather like saying a person with no kidney function left is fine because he is still doing his job. The measurement of "wellness" is completely inappropriate if the lack of working kidneys is ignored and the only thing you measure to determine health is whether the person is at his desk working.

Chemical companies have recently started to do "testing" and now claim that they have data showing that their toxic chemicals do not kill beneficial organisms in the soil. The truth is that they chose methods for those studies that cannot detect 99.999% or more of the beneficial organisms that live in soil. Their data show that no change in organism numbers occurs between the control with no toxic chemical added and the treatment in which toxic chemicals are applied. But the plate count method they use basically can only detect pathogenic bacteria and fungi. Therefore what they are actually showing is that their toxic chemicals can no longer kill the pathogenic organisms in soil that the toxic chemical used to be able to reduce in number. Toxic chemicals are no longer effective in most cases, based on the studies these companies paid someone to perform.

2. All evidence points to the fact that all pesticides kill a broader range of organisms than just the so-called target organism. The only way pesticide companies can try to claim that their chemicals have no effect on nontarget organisms is if the methods used to prove this claim do not in fact detect nontarget organisms. For example, if companies use plate count methods to assess organisms, these methods do not detect nontarget organisms. Again, be careful of the so-called science used to demonstrate something. Just because the terms "control" and "treatment" are used, and replicated testing has been done, this does not mean that the methods were appropriate for assessing the problem.

3. Hanna Instruments has EC meters and chlorine testing kits. Chloramine presence can be determined by a water testing company or by calling your local water district office. When using an EC meter, the levels of salt may be measured in a variety of different units such as µS/cm, mS/cm, or dS/cm. Be very careful when looking at EC values because the units µS/cm are different from mS/cm by a factor of 1,000. If you have 100 µS/cm, it could also be reported as 0.1 mS/cm (move the decimal point three places left and change the unit) or as 0.01 cS/cm. Sometimes chemical salesmen will disguise extremely high salt materials by reporting the information as dS/cm. Scientific units can be confusing if you aren't familiar with them, so check with someone you trust when these issues come up. Do not rely on the person trying to sell you something to explain clearly.

4. You need to determine what beneficial organisms should be added when planting gardens, crops, lawns, or pastures. Assess the food web in the soil to determine whether organisms need to be added. Then determine whether organisms should be mixed into the soil or if they can just be applied to the soil surface. Once organisms are applied, testing will be needed to make sure they survived the trip to your soil. Testing will be needed to make sure they continue to do their jobs over time and the right balance is maintained. For assistance in assessing organisms in your growing system, please call Soil Foodweb Inc. at (541) 752-5066. They have consultants that can work with you. They can provide testing services or provide training or manuals that you can use to learn how to do your own testing.

5. Fungi should still be at least 300 mg, while bacteria should be above 400 mg, per gram of soil. The balance is what is critical; bacteria should be a quarter higher in biomass then fungi for these types of plants.

6. Shrubs, perennial flowers, and herbs are plants that need 300–400 mg or more of a wide array of species of beneficial fungi but only need 300 mg of true bacteria. Perennial plants in general don't do well if the bacteria are actinobacteria, as many actinobacteria appear to suppress mycorrhizal fungi.

7. Some testing using direct microscopy is recommended to determine what is lacking and when the problem is fixed.

8. Test using direct microscope methods to ascertain when the dormant bacteria, fungi, protozoa, and nematodes have become active and are functioning again.

9. Check with your water district for recommendations for water testing facilities in your region. The Soil Foodweb Lab has microorganism testing facilities around the world.

10. Testing is needed to ensure that the organisms and the conditions are right for recovery to occur.

11. The process of returning your system to a condition of health can be rapid and cost a fair amount of money ($100 to $500 per acre depending on just how bad the soil was to start with), or it can take time but be nearly cost-free. If you make your own compost tea, it can be fairly inexpensive, costing $10 to $20 per acre.

We must learn to respect and live according to
the basic biological laws of nature. ~ Jim Fowler

Index

A

abnormal growth, 20
actinobacteria, 70
aerobic compost
    beneficial organisms, 47
    function of, 3
    process of making, 26–27
air pollution, 42
ammonium nitrate, 13
amoebae, 7
anaerobic organisms, 25, 51
annual flowers, 37–38

B

bacteria
    actinobacteria, 70
    anaerobic bacteria, 51
    balance of, 5
    in manure, 27
    mineral retention in soil, 28
    for plantings, 36–37, 70
    protective barriers, 6
    soil compaction problems and, 51
    soil predators and, 7
    toxic chemicals and, 11
beneficial organisms. See also specific
  organisms
    in aerobic compost, 47
    balance of, 5
    compost tea and, 53
    decomposition of toxic residuals due to,
      13, 56, 57, 58
    function of, 5–7
    nutrient cycling and, 7, 21–22, 29, 43, 46
    organic matter and, 25
    planting and transplanting, 36, 70
    recovery timeframe of soil, 59
    root systems and, 28, 45
    soil structure, 49
    tests of, 70
biennial flowers, 37
biocontrol organisms, 52
brewers for compost tea, 60

C

carbon-block filters, 67–68
certification of organic products, 16
chemical companies, 21, 45, 69
chemical fertilizers
    decomposition and, 57
    drawbacks of, 8
    gradual reduction of, 41–42, 45
    ingredients of, 13
    salt levels in, 13–14
    soil recovery process, 13
chloramine, 67, 69
chlorine, 66–67
compaction of soil, 44, 50–51, 54
compost
    adding nutrients to, 44
    aerobic, 3, 26–27, 47
    airflow to plant stems and, 32
    cost effectiveness of, 59–60
    dead plant material, 63
    function of, 8, 43
    per acre application of, 43, 70
    periodic application of, 39
    potting annual flowers with, 38
    replenishment of fungi with, 37
    root systems and, 34
compost extract
    decomposition of toxic residuals and, 56
    periodic application of, 39
    replenishment of fungi with, 37
compost tea
    brewer for, 60
    cost effectiveness of, 59–60, 70
    decomposition of toxic residuals and, 56
    delivery through watering system, 54
    for disease prevention, 40
    as environmentally friendly, 16
    in fall soil preparation, 62
    on foliage, 52
    organic nutrients and, 42
    periodic application of, 39
    potting annual flowers with, 38
    protection from air pollution, 42
    rebalancing of growing systems and, 32

replenishment of fungi with, 37
soaking root systems, 36
in spring soil preparation, 64
for trees, 40, 54–56
costs of soil recovery, 59–60, 70
crop systems, 36, 70

D

decomposition
of dead plant material, 63
of toxic residuals, 13, 56, 57, 58
during winter, 62
disease organisms
compost tea and suppression of, 40
decomposition during winter and, 62
function of, 22
healthy plants vs., 20
dried fish, 35

E

earthworms
in manure, 27
pesticide effects on, 11
plant nutrients and, 7
EC meters, 17, 68, 69
ecosystems in nature, 7
Edible Forest Gardens (Jacke), 26
electrical conductivity (EC) levels, 17, 27, 68
environmentally friendly products, 15–17
extract. See compost extract

F

fall soil preparation, 62
feeding plants, 39–47. See also compost
compost application, 43–44
compost tea and disease suppression,
40–41
foliar applications, 40
microbes, 40–41, 47
observing plants for disease, 41
reduction of chemical fertilizers, 41–42,
45
soil tests and, 45–46
spraying nutrients on plants, 39
tillage of soil, 44, 46

feedlot manure, 26
fertilizers. See chemical fertilizers; compost
fish flakes, 35
flagellates, 7
flowers, 37–38, 64, 70
fungi
balance of, 5
compost and, 37
humic acid formation, 24
in manure, 27
mineral retention in soil, 28
mycorrhizal fungal spores, 36–37, 55, 70
for plantings, 36–37, 70
protective barriers, 6
soil predators and, 7
toxic chemicals and, 11
fungicides, 10

G

Gardening With Nature. See also specific
aspects
definition of, 1–2
process of, 3–7
grain material, 35
green cover crops, 63
growing system, assessment of, 9–14
gypsum, 13

H

Hanna Instruments, 69
healthy plants, 19–22, 27
herbicides, 10, 46
herbs, 36–37, 70
humic acid
compost and, 44
as environmentally friendly, 16
as fertilizer, 8
fungi and, 24
salt levels and, 24–25
humus, 24, 25, 67

I

inorganic fertilizers. See chemical fertilizers
inorganic nutrients
elimination of, 45

microbes as replacement for, 43
insect pests
    as messengers of underlying problem, 11
    pesticides and, 22
    unhealthy plants and, 20

J

Jacke, David, *Edible Forest Gardens*, 26

L

lawns, 36, 70
lime, 13
liquid compost. See compost extract;
  compost tea
liquid humus, 67
litter layer, 44

M

manure, 26
microarthropods, 7, 11, 28, 43, 53
microbes
    disease resistant plants and, 40
    necessity of, 28
    in plant feedings, 40–41, 47
    as replacement for inorganic nutrients,
      43
microscope methods, 56, 70
mulch, 44
mycorrhizae, 16
mycorrhizal fungal spores. See also fungi
    actinobacteria suppression of, 70
    in compost tea for trees, 55
    planting and transplanting, 36–37
    seed preparation and, 36

N

National Organic Program (NOP), 16
natural ecosystems, 7
nematodes, beneficial
    function of, 7, 43
    harmful nematodes vs., 20
    improving nutrient deficiencies, 53
    in manure, 27
    microscope methods and, 70
    nutrient cycling, 28

toxic chemicals and, 11
nonbeneficial organisms, 5. See also specific
  types
N-P-K tests, 45
"nuke-em" approach, 11
nutrient cycling. See also soluble nutrients
    due to beneficial organisms, 7, 21–22, 29,
      43, 46
    soil composition and, 24, 29
nutrient deficiency
    compost liquids for, 53
    soil compaction problems and, 51
    tests of, 21–22

O

organic, definition of, 16
organic matter
    beneficial organisms and, 25
    nutrients in, 43
    percentage of in soil composition, 24–25,
      41
    root systems, 45, 53
    soluble nutrients and, 45
organic microbe food, 35. See also specific
  types
organic products, 15–17
organically approved seal, 16
overtillage. See tillage of soil

P

pastures, 36, 70
perennial flowers
    adding beneficial organisms, 36–37, 70
    spring soil preparation, 64
pesticides
    decomposition of toxic residuals, 57
    drawbacks of, 10
    drifting from neighbor use, 58
    insect pests and, 22
    misleading testing by chemical
      companies, 69
plant food, 35
plant pathogens. See disease organisms
plant succession process, 29–31
planting and transplanting, 33–38
    adding beneficial organisms, 36–37, 70

annual flowers, 37–38
caring for soil, 35
crop systems, 36
herbs, 36–37, 70
lawns, 36
organic microbe food, 35
pastures, 36
root systems, 34
seed preparation, 36
shrubs, 36–37, 70
soaking root systems, 36
soil composition, 33
plants. See also specific types
airflow to stems, 32
feeding of, 39–47
healthy, 19–20, 22, 27
planting and transplanting, 33–38
root systems, 22, 28
stress symptoms of, 20–21, 52, 53
unhealthy, 10–11, 20–22, 52
plate count methods, 69
potting mix, 38
protozoa
in food web, 29
in manure, 27
microscope methods and, 70
nutrient cycling in soil, 28, 43
nutrient deficiency and, 53
toxic chemicals and, 11

R

reverse osmosis systems, 67–68
root systems
beneficial organisms, 28, 45
compost and, 34
oxygen requirements of, 49
resistance to disease, 22
soil compaction problems and, 54–55
soil structure and, 29
rototilling. See tillage of soil

S

sales pitches by chemical companies, 21, 45, 69
salt levels
appearance of leaves and, 25
in chemical fertilizers, 13–14
in feedlot manure, 26
humic acid and, 24–25
misleading testing by chemical companies, 69
tests of, 17, 27, 69
in water supplies, 68
sea kelp
as environmentally friendly, 16
as fertilizer, 8
testing for salt levels in, 17
transplanting and, 35
seal of approval, for organic products, 16
seasonal soil preparation, 61–63
seed preparation, 36
shrubs, 36–37, 70
snow accumulation, 63
soil food web
Gardening With Nature and, 4
in potting mixes, 38
soil structure and, 24, 57
succession process, 29
testing of, 70
Soil Foodweb Inc., 70
soil predators, 4, 7, 21
soil preparation, 23–32
during fall, 62
for new plantings, 33
organic matter in, 24–25, 41, 43, 45, 53
planting and transplanting, 33–38
during spring, 64
tree health and, 56
during winter, 62, 63
soil quality. See also beneficial organisms
aerobic compost and, 3, 47
balanced, 3, 24, 32, 51, 53
compaction issues, 44, 50–51, 54
effects of tillage on, 44, 46, 50
litter layer, 44
recovery timeframe, 59
replenishment of, 32
tests of, 21, 45, 56, 70
soil structure
beneficial organisms, 49
delivery of compost tea and, 54
effect of tillage on, 50

healthy plants and, 27
root systems, 29
soil food web and, 24, 57
water and, 8, 49
soluble nutrients
leaching into water sources, 46
overemphasis on, 43, 45–46
tests of, 21
spring soil preparation, 64
stream/lake/river contamination, 10
stress symptoms of plants, 20–21, 52, 53
succession process, 29–31

T
tests
for chlorine in water, 66
for levels of beneficial organisms, 70
microbiological analysis of soil, 56, 70
misleading testing by chemical
companies, 21, 45, 69
for N-P-K, 45
for nutrient deficiency, 21–22
for reestablishment of beneficial
organisms, 43, 70
for salt levels, 17, 27, 69
of soil chemistry, 21, 45
of soil food web, 70
tillage of soil, 44, 46, 50
toxic chemicals. See also chemical fertilizers;
specific toxic chemicals
decomposition of, 13, 56
drawbacks of, 10–12
frequency of use, 12
misleading testing by chemical
companies, 21, 45, 69
transplanting. See planting and
transplanting
trees
compost tea for, 40, 54–56
mycorrhizal fungi spores and, 55

U
underlying cause of problems, 10–11
unhealthy plants, 10–11, 20–22, 52. See also
disease organisms

W
water
compaction and accumulation of, 50
soil structure and, 8, 49
water quality
chloramine and, 67, 69
chlorine and, 66–67
leaching of soluable nutrients, 46
salt levels, 13–14, 68
toxic chemical contamination, 10
watering systems
delivery of compost tea through, 54
filtering chlorine out, 67
weeds
anaerobic bacteria and, 51
as messengers of soil health, 12
toxic chemicals and, 12
unhealthy plants and, 20
winter soil preparation, 62, 63
worm castings, 16, 44

Everything in nature contains all the power of nature.
~ Ralph Waldo Emerson

About The Authors

Carole Rollins, PhD

Carole Ann Rollins is co-owner (with her husband, James Eddington), of Nature Technologies International LLC. The company produces Organic Gardening Products—Nature's Solution compost tea, ancient humate, sea kelp, mycorrhizae, worm castings, and compost tea brewers. She co-authored two books and a poster with Elaine Ingham: *Adding Biology for Soil and Hydroponic Systems* and *The Microbe Manual* and The Microbe Poster. She compiled and edited *The Field Guide I and II for Actively Aerated Compost Tea* for Elaine Ingham. Contact Info: Nature's Solution, P.O. Box 1519, Novato, CA 94948, 415-898-5895; website: http://www.nature-technologies.com; email: info@nature-technologies.com.

Elaine Ingham, PhD

Elaine Ingham is Chief Scientist for the Rodale Institute and founder of Soil Foodweb Inc., an international laboratory system that assesses the balance of bacteria, fungi, protozoa, nematodes, and mycorrhizal fungi in all materials. The major emphasis of her work is to return health to soil, so that natural nutrient retention, nutrient cycling, and disease suppression occur, allowing nutrient-dense, maximum yields of the desired plants without requiring use of pesticides or inorganic fertilizers. Contact Info: Sustainable Studies Institute, 635 SW Western Avenue, Corvallis, OR 97330; 541-752-5066, website: www.sustainablestudies.org, email: elaine.ingham@rodaleinst.org.

When one tugs at a single thing in nature;
he finds it attached to the rest of the world. ~ John Muir